action science

Genetics and evolution

Joan O'Sullivan, William Merrick

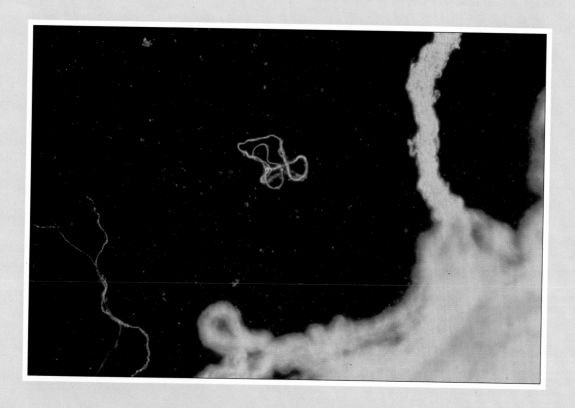

• The same but different • Dividing cells • Inheritance • Selection •
• Genetic engineering • Four case studies •

Oxford University Press 1993

Oxford University Press, Walton Street, Oxford OX2 6DP

Oxford New York Toronto Delhi Bombay Calcutta Madras Karachi
Kuala Lumpur Singapore Hong Kong Tokyo Nairobi Dar es Salaam
Cape Town Melbourne Auckland Madrid
and associated companies in
Berlin Ibadan

Oxford is a trade mark of Oxford University Press

ISBN 0 19 914365 X

Typeset in 10½/14 pt Monotype Joanna and Bell Gothic by
MS Filmsetting Ltd, Frome, Somerset

First published 1993

Printed in Hong Kong

A CIP catalogue record for this book is available from the British Library

Coordinating Editors: David Appleby, Alan Jarvis,
William Merrick, Joan O'Sullivan

Acknowledgements

Photographs
The publishers wish to thank the following for permission to reproduce
transparencies:
Allsport pp7 (T), 52 (T); **BBC** p30 (L); **Biophotos** pp13, 21 (T.L.), 31 (B);
Bruce Coleman pp7 (B), 11, 15, 29 (T.M.), 35, 53 (B.L.); **Mary Evans Photo
Library** pp16 (T), 32 (T), 49, 53 (B.R.); **Families of the design and
editorial team** p5; **Robert Harding** p20 (R); **Holt Studios** p9 (B.R.); **Chris
Moore** pp9, 29; **Joan O'Sullivan** pp27, 52 (B); **Oxford Scientific Films** pp9
(T.R.), 18 (B), 21 (T.R., M.L., B.R.); 30 (R), 31 (T), 32 (B), 33, 53 (T.R.);
O.U.P./Franklin Berger; O.U.P./Chris Honeywell p4; **O.U.P./Zul Mukhida**
p20 (L); **Radio Times/B. Robinson** p17 (B).

Illustrations are by:
Isabell Bowring (c/o Temple Rogers) pp7, 10, 23 (B.R.), 26, 51; **Joanna
Cameron** pp28, 30; **Martina Farrow** p55 (B.R.); **Sarah Govia** pp22 (B), 24,
26; **David Holmes** pp46–47; **Susan McCormick** pp31 (R), 33, 43, 53;
Patricia Moffett pp8 (B), 36; **Chris Price** p54; **Adam Stower** p48; **Michael
Worthington** pp6, 8 (T), 10, 35, 50; **Galina Zolfaghhari** pp 14–16, 19, 22
(T), 23, 25, 26, 31 (L), 34, 39–42, 44–47, 55 (T).

How to use this book

This book is not intended to be read consecutively from beginning to end. It is designed to give you more active involvement in how to learn science.

The book is made up of six sections. Each section contains four different types of page which you should use in different ways:

✸ Visual stimulus
These highly illustrated pages are designed to bring you into the topic in an interesting way and get you thinking. Use the *Factfile* and other resources to help you with the activities.

ⓘ Factfile
These pages bring together essential information about the topic of the section. You should dip into the *Factfile* as and when you need to and use it to help you to answer the questions in the rest of the section. The *Key facts* box summarizes the main points you should have learnt from the section. The *Factfile* is also helpful for revision.

✍ Background reading
This contains one or two articles to give you an understanding of how the science you are learning fits into the outside world. These often deal with topical and contentious issues. It is important that you should grasp the underlying science in such issues so that you can make an informed judgement. Use the activities at the end to test your understanding.

ⓘ Questions and activities
As you answer the questions on these pages, you will be taken through the facts and ideas covered in the section, helping you to learn them. There are various kinds of activities and your teacher will help you to choose the right ones for you.

✚ Extension pages
These can be found at the end of the book. They allow you to practice the important skill of making sense of information in the form of words, graphs or tables and using this data to answer questions.

Contents

No two the same

All these people are members of the same species **Homo sapiens**, so in many ways they are all very much the same – they all have two eyes, two legs, etc. They are also different from one another in some ways. They show a lot of **variation**. For example there are many different heights, weights, skin colours, and so on.

A Discuss the picture in pairs and make a list as shown below of all the ways in which people vary. Try to put in a rough idea of the range of types.

Characteristic	From	To
Height	1.50 m	1.90 m
Eye colour	Blue	Brown
. . . etc.		

B Pick one of the characteristics from your list. Choose one which you can measure. Survey your class to see how much this characteristic varies. Record your results in a tally chart similar to this one:

Height (m)	Number of people
1.50–1.54	I (1)
1.55–1.59	III (3)
1.60–1.64	⊞ (5)
. . . etc.	

Who do you take after?

Do you look more like your mother or your father? Perhaps people say you remind them of one of your grandparents. Are you like your brothers, sisters and cousins? Some things seem to 'run in the family'.

Far left, top to bottom: Three generations of one family at the same age. Left: Parents and children. Above: Siblings.

A Think about some families you know. Are there any special features that they share that give them a 'family resemblance'?

B Collect photographs of members of your own family. Make a display of them to show how you all resemble one another.

Variation

Human beings come in a whole range of shapes and sizes. There are many detailed differences of eye, hair and skin colour. We all have different abilities. In the whole world nobody exists who is exactly the same as you. The same is true for every other kind of living thing.

We use the word **variation** to describe all these differences between members of a species.

All plants and animals show variation. The bluebells in a wood might all look the same at first, but if we look closer there are many ways to tell them apart. Even flies are individuals!

Discontinuous variation

Sometimes we can divide characteristics into clear types. Human beings may be brown eyed or blue eyed, and it is rare to see any colours in between. Pea flowers are either red or white. There may be more than two types. There are four main human blood groups called A, B, AB and O. Everyone belongs to one of these groups; nobody is in between.

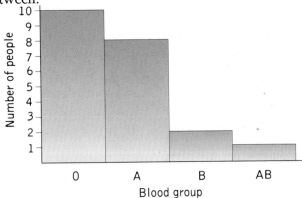

The table gives more examples of characteristics showing **discontinuous variation**.

Organism	Characteristic	Type
Garden pea	Height Seed shape	Tall or dwarf Round or wrinkled
Peppered moth	Colour	Dark or light body and wings
Fruit fly	Eye colour	Red or white
Humans	Sex	Male or female

Continuous variation

Many characteristics do not fall into clear types. In everyday speech we might talk about 'short' or 'tall' people, but in reality there are many sizes in between. When a characteristic has a smooth range we say it shows **continuous variation**. This shape of curve depicts a **normal distribution**. It shows that the average height is the most common. Fewer people have the heights that are further away from the average. Many characteristics show continuous variation. Examples are height and weight, and also many abilities, such as how fast you can run.

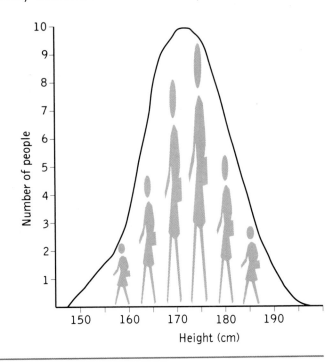

Nature or nurture?

Why are people so different from one another? Is a tall person tall because their parents were tall, or is it because they ate plenty of good food while they were growing up? In other words, do we inherit our own special characteristics from our parents, or are they caused by the environment we live in? For most characteristics the answer seems to be that both these things play a part. People do take after their parents in all sorts of ways, but even if someone had two very tall parents they might still be quite small if they did not get enough to eat, or if they were very ill while they were young. Our inheritance (nature) and the conditions we live in (nurture) work together to make us what we are.

Athletes may inherit their strength, but they must train as well.

What is a species?

A **species** is a group of animals that can breed together. A species may show a very wide range of variation. All the domestic dogs, from an Alsatian to a Poodle, are members of the same species. They look very different, but they can mate and give birth to cross-breed dogs which are perfectly healthy.

One species — wide variation.

It is the same for plants. All apple trees belong to the same species. Different varieties can be cross-bred, and this produces even more variation: new types of apples are made in this way.

Members of two different species cannot breed. Dogs and cats just will not mate with one another.

Even if they did, there would be no offspring. If pollen from grass blows into a rose flower it cannot fertilize it.

An exception to the rule?

Sometimes two different species will mate and produce babies. A horse and a donkey can be mated, and the result is a mule. There have been cases in zoos of lions and tigers producing cubs ('ligers'!). These **hybrid** animals seem to break our rule that only members of the same species can breed. In fact they help to prove it. The offspring are always sterile. They cannot breed themselves; they are dead ends. We have to improve the wording of the rule to:

A species is a group of animals or plants which can breed to produce fertile offspring.

A mule: a cross between horse and donkey.

Classification

Life on our planet is enormously varied. There are millions of different species. To make it easier to study them scientists like to think about them in groups. Putting things into groups is called classification.

To start with we can split living things into two main groups – animals and plants. These big groups can then be divided again. The animal **kingdom** is divided into two: animals without backbones (**invertebrates**) and animals with backbones (**vertebrates**). The animals without backbones are then divided into **phyla** such as molluscs (snails, oysters and octopi) and arthropods (crabs, insects, spiders). Animals with backbones belong to a phylum called **chordates**. This splits into five main **classes**: fish, amphibians, reptiles, birds and mammals. Each group goes on splitting. Classes are broken into **orders**, orders into **families**, families into **genera**, and finally genera split up into **species**.

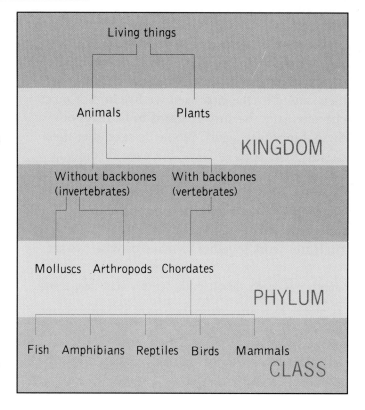

Classifying a lion

Lions belong to the species *leo*. Lions share the genus *Felis* with tigers, lynxes and all of the other cats.

Species: *leo*. Lions only.

Genus: *Felis*
Lions and all cats; tigers, pumas, domestic cats.

Family: *Felidae*
The cats and Smilodon (the sabre-toothed tiger).

Order: *Carnivora*
Meat-eaters. Cats, dogs, bears, weasels.

Class: *Mammalia*
Warm-blooded, furry animals feeding their babies on milk. Carnivores, and horses, cows, monkeys, dolphins.

Phylum: *Chordata*
Animals with backbones. Mammals, birds, reptiles, amphibians and fish.

Kingdom: *Animals*
All animals. Those with backbones and those without.

Full name – *Felis leo*.

Felis catus.

Cabbages

The variation in a species can be very large indeed. Sometimes the members of a species can look so different from one another that we can hardly recognize them. This has been especially true since human beings began breeding plants and animals to use in the garden or on the farm.

All the vegetables pictured on this page are members of the same species, Brassica oleracia. The varieties look very different, but they can all be bred with one another. For thousands of years farmers all over the world have been improving them to make them larger and better to eat.

They are all descended from an ancestor called the wild cabbage. It is still found all over Europe, and you can see it growing on cliffs by the sea in England and Wales. The leaves look quite like the ones on garden cabbages, but they are not collected into a 'head'. They are also too tough to eat.

The garden cabbage was probably first domesticated about 1000 years BC in one of the countries around the Mediterranean. Ancient Greeks and Romans grew them in their gardens.

Brussels sprouts have been bred from garden cabbages. We find them mentioned in Belgian farming books over 700 years ago. They were called spruyten.

Cauliflowers are a little older. An Arabic book written in the 12th century called them Syrian cabbages. Our word cauliflower reminds us that the part we eat is the modified flower of the plant. Broccoli is a close relative. Again we eat the flowering part, which is much more 'fleshy' than the normal flowers of the wild ancestor.

All this variation has been selected by farmers, but it is not enough to turn the vegetables into new species. The new types are just called 'varieties'.

New varieties of farm animals are called 'breeds'.

Wild cabbage.

Garden cabbage.

Cauliflower.

Brussels sprouts.

Broccoli.

● Choose one species of farm animal which has several breeds, and make a display of its history. What was the original wild type? What types do we have now? Who bred them? How are the new types better than the originals? Are there any problems with the new breeds?

Questions and activities

A Copy and complete these sentences using words from the list to help.

**breed   different   genus
kingdom   species   variation**

A _____ is a group of similar animals or plants which can _____ together. All members of a species are slightly _____. The differences are called _____. A number of similar species can be put together to make up a bigger group called a _____. The largest group to which all animals belong is called the animal _____.

B Go back to the tally chart you made in the experiment on page 4. Turn your results into a bar graph, like the ones in the *Factfile*.

a Did the characteristic you chose show continuous or discontinuous variation?
b Look at all the results from your class. Sort the types of variation into continuous or discontinuous. Which type of variation is found most often?

C Try making a bar chart to show the variation in science test results for your group. They will show continuous variation.

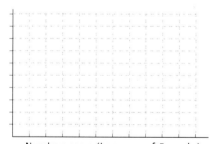

Numbers score (in groups of 5 marks)

a Work out the average score by adding up all of the results and dividing by the number of pupils in your group.

$$\text{Average} = \frac{\text{total for group}}{\text{number in group}}.$$

Does the tallest bar on your graph contain the average score?
b Discuss this question with your teacher: What is the main cause of the variation in test results; natural scientific ability (nature) or how hard you work (nurture)?

D Make a poster display to show the five classes of vertebrates (fish, amphibians, reptiles, birds and mammals). You could work in groups, and each group could work on one class. Try to find pictures of as many different members of each class as possible, to show the whole range of variation. On each poster write a list of the features of that class. For example:

Birds:
Fly
Have feathers
Lay eggs with hard shells, etc.

Making a key

When scientists want to find out the name of a plant or an animal they have never seen before they use a key. This is a book which asks simple questions about the animal or plant, and then leads them to its name. Suppose we had this information about garden birds:

	Size (cm)	Feather colours
Starling	22	Glossy purple and green; speckled
Songthrush	22	Brown back, cream breast
Chaffinch	16	Pink face and breast; white bars on wings
Robin	14	Grey head; red face and breast

Robin.

Chaffinch.

A key to identify the birds might start like this:

```
                 Is it larger than 20 cm?
                 Yes            No
      Does it have glossy        Does it have white
   purple and green feathers?     bars on its wings?
     Yes         No              Yes         No
   Starling   Songthrush       Chaffinch    Robin
```

Then we turn the 'tree' into a written 'key'.

1. Is it larger than 20 cm?
    If yes go to 2.
    If no go to 3.

2. Does it have glossy purple and green feathers?
    If yes ... starling
    If no ... songthrush

3. Does it have white bars on its wings?
    If yes ... chaffinch
    If no ... robin

● Make up a key to identify these wild flowers.

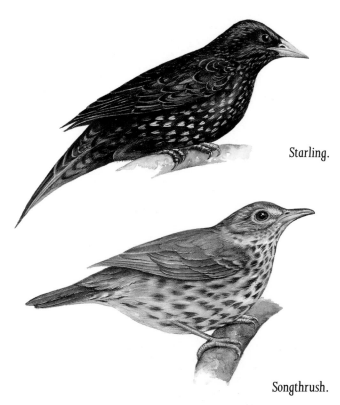

Starling.

Songthrush.

	Flowers	Leaves	Height (cm)
White deadnettle (*Lamium album*)	Large, white	Hairy No sting	60
Purple deadnettle (*Lamium purpureum*)	Small, purple	Hairy No sting	15
Stinging nettle (*Urtica dioica*)	Small, green	Hairy Sting	60
Small nettle (*Urtica urens*)	Small, green	Hairy Sting	30

Would you touch this one?

Cells

Plants and animals are both made of cells. The cells of plants are similar to those of animals in many ways, but there are some important differences.

A Study the photographs of human cheek cells and plant leaf cells. Use your school microscopes to look at some more animal and plant cells.

● Make drawings of the cells as you see them under the microscope. Use the diagrams in the *Factfile* to label these parts: cell membrane, cytoplasm, nucleus.

B Some organisms called protozoa have bodies made up of a single cell. Find out about protozoa in library books and make a display about two or three different types. Pay special attention to the way they reproduce.

Inside the nucleus

A special stain and a good microscope allow us to see structures inside the nucleus of a cell. They are called **chromosomes**. All cells contain them, but different species have different numbers. Human beings have 46 chromosomes in every cell.

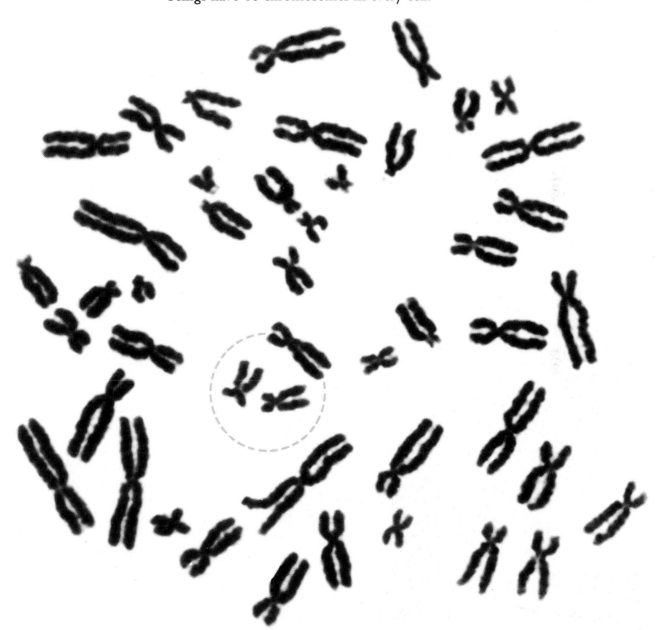

A Look hard at these human chromosomes. There are 46 altogether. They can be put into 23 pairs. One pair has been ringed on the photograph.

Your teacher can give you a photocopy of this picture. Cut it up and sort the chromosomes to make 23 pairs. Stick the pieces into your notebook.

B Use reference books to find out how many pairs of chromosomes different plants and animals have. Is it true that simpler organisms have fewer chromosomes?

Cell, chromosome, gene

Inside every plant or animal cell there is a **nucleus**. The nucleus contains the thread-like **chromosomes**. Chromosomes are always in pairs. There are different numbers of chromosomes in different organisms. Fruit flies have only four pairs, but human beings have 23 pairs.

Chromosomes are rows of chemical molecules, rather like a necklace made from a string of separate beads. Each individual bead in the chromosome chain is called a **gene**. Genes are the 'plans' for making the animal or plant. They spell out, in a chemical code, the instructions for building the organism. There will be genes for size, colour, shape; every part is described. The chemical that genes are made of is called **DNA**, which is short for deoxyribonucleic acid!

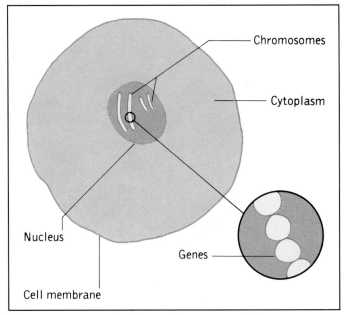

This imaginary animal cell has only two pairs of chromosomes.

Gametes and fertilization

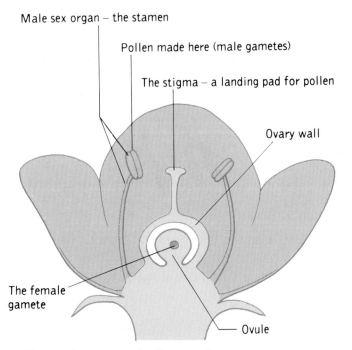

The reproductive parts of a flowering plant.

Animals and plants inherit their appearance from both their parents. This is true for all animals and plants. This is because the offspring get half of their chromosomes from each parent. The chromosomes carry genes from the parents to the children. For example, the parents might have genes which give them blue eyes. The children will be given those genes, and so they will have blue eyes too. The chromosomes are passed from parents to offspring in special sex cells called **gametes**. In animals the male gametes are sperm and the female gametes are the eggs. In plants the pollen grains contain the male gametes, and the female gametes are the ovules (which is the Latin word for eggs). Gametes are special reproductive cells whose job is to carry genes from one generation to the next. Fertilization occurs when the male and female gametes fuse to form a new cell or **zygote**. The zygote divides many times to produce the new animal or plant.

Mitosis – cell division for growth

Every living thing, including you, begins as a
fertilized egg. This first cell divides and grows until
it becomes an adult with millions of cells. In human
beings, the first cell has 23 pairs of chromosomes.
It splits to make two cells which also have 23 pairs.
Just before a cell splits, it makes a copy of its
chromosomes, so there will be one full set for each
of the two new cells. Every cell in your body
contains a perfect copy of the 23 pairs of
chromosomes. This kind of cell division is called
mitosis. It happens when cells are made for growth
or to mend injuries.

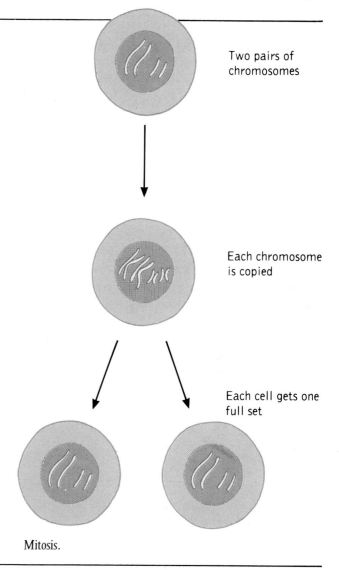

Two pairs of
chromosomes

Each chromosome
is copied

Each cell gets one
full set

Mitosis.

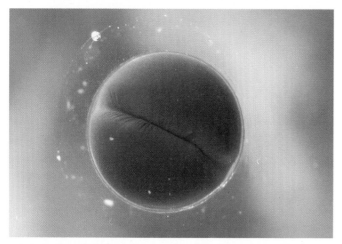

After the first division.

Meiosis – a special cell division to make gametes

When a sperm fuses with an egg the father's
chromosomes are merged with those of the mother.
This could cause problems: Since both the father's
and mother's cells have 46 chromosomes each, the
baby would have 92 – twice as many as it needs!

To avoid this sperm and eggs are made in a special
way. They are only given *half* a set of chromosomes.
Every gamete has only 23 *single* chromosomes – one
from each of the 23 pairs. This special cell division
is called **meiosis**. When the sperm fertilizes the
egg, we end up with the proper 23 *pairs*: 23 singles
from the mother and 23 singles from the father.
The baby gets half its genes from each parent.

The gametes of all animals and plants are made by
meiosis. They always have half the normal number
of chromosomes.

Fruit flies with their four pairs of chromosomes in
each cell would have four single chromosomes in
each gamete. Another example is a pea plant with
seven pairs of chromosomes in each cell. This
would have seven single chromosomes in each
gamete.

This cell has two
pairs of
chromosomes

Gametes only have half
a set of chromosomes

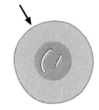

Meiosis.

The inheritance of sex

Henry VIII wanted a son to be king after him. He is supposed to have divorced his first wife Catherine of Aragon and executed his second, Anne Boleyn, because they gave him daughters. Jane Seymour, his third wife did have a son, Prince Edward. Henry thought that the mother determined the sex of the baby. Was he right?

Whether a baby is a boy or a girl depends on its chromosomes. Of the 23 pairs of human chromosomes, 22 are exactly the same in both sexes. The 23rd pair decides the sex of the baby. A microscope shows that the chromosomes are different in the two sexes.

Making gametes

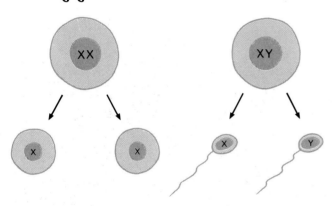

When female XX cells divide they make eggs with one X chromosome each. When male XY cells divide, half the sperm will contain a single X, and the other half will contain a single Y.

Fertilization

When a couple make love, the man produces about 500 million sperm. Half of them will be X and half will be Y. Whether the baby is a boy or a girl is just a matter of chance. It depends on which type of sperm first enters the egg.

Perhaps if Henry had known something about genetics things may have worked out more happily for his wives. It was the King's sperm, not the Queens' eggs, that produced the daughters!

If an X sperm enters the egg first, the baby will be a girl. If a Y sperm wins the 'race', the baby will be a boy.

◀ *Henry VIII.*

Female: *The chromosomes in the 23rd pair are the same. Each is an X chromosome, so we write 'XX' for a female cell.*
▼

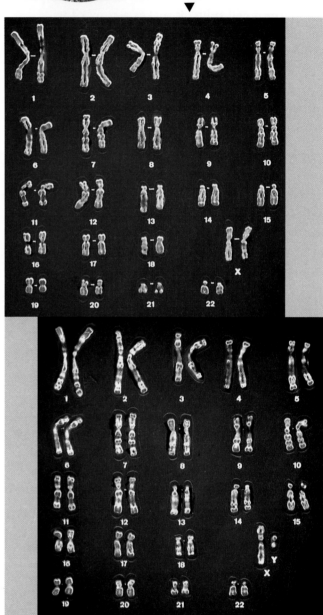

Male: *One chromosome in the 23rd pair is an X, but the other is a smaller Y chromosome. We write 'XY' for a male cell.*

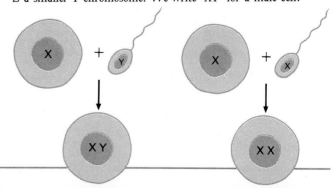

Inherited diseases

Some diseases are caused by the chromosomes and the genes they carry. Genes control outer features such as our size, colour and general appearance. They are also the plans for our internal organs such as heart, lungs, liver and so on. If there is a fault in the plans for any of these important organs they will not work properly, and the person will be ill.

Down's Syndrome — problems with a whole chromosome

Some people are born with 47 chromosomes instead of the normal 46. Very often the problem is with the 21st chromosome. The photograph shows that there are three of them instead of two. This is called **trisomy**. People with this illness suffer from a number of difficulties. They are likely to be well below average intelligence, although many can be helped by special education. There is also a characteristic appearance of the face and eyes. Heart problems are common.

Down's Syndrome affects about one baby in 650, and is more common in babies born to older mothers. It seems that something goes wrong with cell division as the eggs are made (see **meiosis**), giving an egg with an extra chromosome.

▶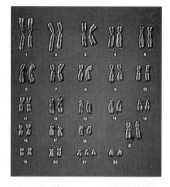
Down's chromosomes. One group of chromosomes is triple instead of double.

A family with three adopted children with Down's Syndrome and a child with Cerebral Palsy.

Huntingdon's Chorea — a problem with a single gene

This is a rare disease which people inherit from their parents, although it only shows up when the patient is about 30 or 40 years old. Cells in the brain begin to degenerate, and the patient becomes fidgety and clumsy. Their personality alters, and they become moody and depressed. Memory and intelligence are damaged. Eventually patients become totally disabled, and then die. All of this is caused by one damaged gene.

A There are many other inherited diseases. Choose one from this list to research into, and give a presentation about it.

- Sickle cell anaemia
- Cystic fibrosis
- Phenylketonuria
- Achondroplasia

In your presentation you should describe the symptoms, find out how common it is, and say what can be done for people suffering from it.

B Some health problems come from a combination of inheritance and way of life. An example is coronary heart disease. It can be made worse by bad diet, lack of exercise and smoking, but it also seems to 'run in families'.

What advice would you give to someone who says, "Many people in my family have bad hearts. If I've inherited it too, then I'm stuck with it. I'm not going to worry about my diet."

Questions and activities

A This model shows sperm gathering around a human egg.

Soon one of the sperm will enter the egg. As soon as this happens the cell membrane of the egg changes so that no other sperm can get through. Why is it necessary to stop more than one sperm entering the egg?

B Use microscopes to study the cells of a root tip which has been stained to show up the chromosomes.

Search the slide for some cells which are dividing. They will be near the tip where the root is growing.

Draw some of the cells you can see. Show as much detail of the chromosomes as possible. Use the highest powered objective lens and draw large diagrams.

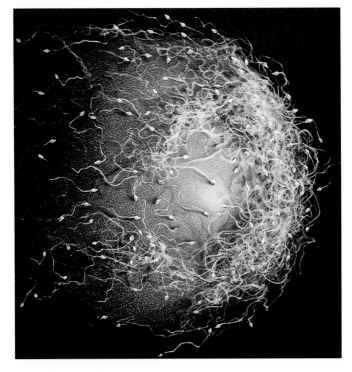

  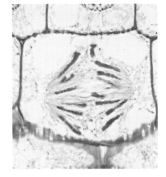

These three photographs show, from left to right, the process of mitosis in an onion root tip cell. The cells have been stained to make the chromosomes clearly visible.

C Cells with the normal double set of chromosomes are called **diploid**. Most cells in an organism are diploid. Cells with a single set (half the normal number) are called **haploid**. Gametes are haploid.

Copy the summary chart and put the correct words and phrases into the boxes.

FERTILIZATION   **MEIOSIS**   **MITOSIS**

Corresponds to mating in animals

Special sex cells (gametes) are made

Growth

	Dipoloid cells divide to make new cells with only half the normal number of chromosomes	
	Two haploid cells fuse together	A new individual begins
POLLINATION	A gamete is transferred from the male part of the flower to the female part	
	Diploid cells divide to make more diploid cells	

D In some cases different numbers of sex chromosomes have been found in humans. For instance some men are XXY. What sex chromosomes could be in the sperm of a man who is XXY? What are the possible sex chromosomes of his children?

E Mr and Mrs Smith have four daughters. They think that their fifth child is more than likely to be a son. Is this so?

Sort it out!

When you are growing, your cells are always dividing into two. You started off as one cell; now you have millions. This kind of cell division is called mitosis.

Each of the new cells is an exact copy of the first one. The first cell had 23 pairs of chromosomes (46 altogether). When it split it made two cells which also had 23 pairs. Just before it splits the cell makes a copy of all the chromosomes, so that there is one full set for each of the new cells.

These pictures show some of the stages as the cell divides. They have been simplified. Only two pairs of chromosomes are shown. The order of the pictures has been jumbled up.

● Sort the pictures out into the correct order. You can copy the pictures, or your teacher may be able to give you some photocopies to cut out and stick in your books.

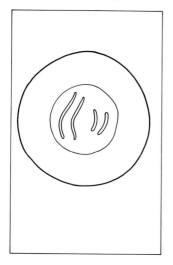

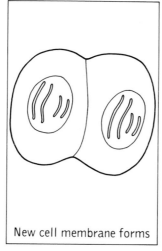

New cell membrane forms

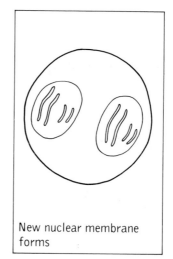

New nuclear membrane forms

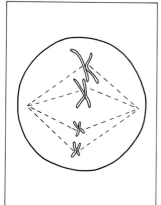

Chromosomes line up on spindles

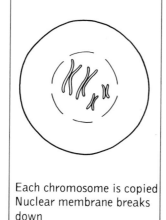

Each chromosome is copied Nuclear membrane breaks down

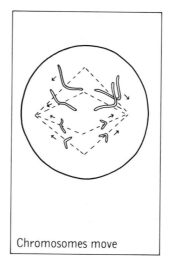

Chromosomes move

Like and unlike

Identical twins occur when an egg splits after fertilization. Their genes are identical. Unlike twins come from two fertilizations, two eggs and two sperm, so their genes are similar but different.

▲ Jane and Kate are identical twins.
Mary and Meg are unlike twins.▶

A Make a list of all the similarities between Jane and Kate. Are there any differences you can spot?

B Make a second list of the similarities and differences you can find between Mary and Meg.

C Suggest some ways you would expect identical twins to differ. What reasons can you think of for these differences?

Changes

Occasionally a pair of normally coloured parents will produce an **albino** child. Albinos have no coloured pigment in their skin, hair or eyes. Albinos occur in all animal groups, and even in some plants.

A Only one in thousands of babies is an albino. What problems do you think the albino boy would have?

B Most other animal groups have albinos. Are there any times when you think this could be an advantage for the animal?

C Parts of a plant may have no pigment. Explain why an albino plant would be unable to survive on its own.

Key facts: inheritance

- Genes can be changed by mutations.
- Genes can be **dominant** or **recessive**.
- Each gene has two expressions or **alleles**, one from the mother and one from the father.
- If the two alleles are different only the dominant one will have an effect.
- **Co-dominance** occurs when both alleles affect the organism.

Mutations

Genes pass on the same characteristics from one generation to the next. On rare occasions a new characteristic appears, such as a fly with a different wing shape or a person with an extra finger. These new characteristics are **mutations** caused by a change in the gene so that its instructions are altered. These mutations can then be passed on to future generations. Usually they are harmful but sometimes a mutant will have an advantage over other organisms and be more likely to survive.

Extra fingers and toes is a fairly common mutation.

Dominant and recessive genes

When a pair of alleles is different or heterozygous, the organism usually only shows one of the characteristics. For example, in humans one allele for brown eyes and one for blue produces a brown-eyed person. The allele for brown eyes is **dominant** to that for blue eyes. The allele for blue eyes is said to be **recessive** and will not affect the organism. Only when both alleles are recessive will a person have blue eyes.

Brown [B]   [B] Brown

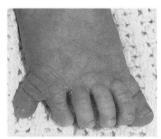
Brown eyes

Brown [B]   [b] Blue

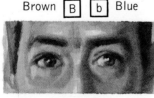
Brown eyes

Blue [b]   [b] Blue

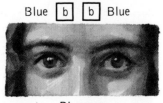
Blue eyes

Alleles

Each chromosome pair has genes for similar features along their length.

The gene for eye colour could be blue, grey, green, brown or hazel. Each of these alternative forms is called an **allele**. If the two alleles on each chromosome pair are the same, the organism is **homozygous** for this feature. If the two alleles are different, the organism is **heterozygous**.

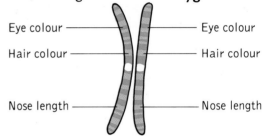

Eye colour ———|———— Eye colour

Hair colour ———|———— Hair colour

Nose length ———|———— Nose length

Phenotype and genotype

The appearance of an organism is known as its **phenotype**, e.g. red flowers, brown fur, blue eyes.

The genes or alleles present are referred to as the **genotype**, e.g. AA, Aa or aa.

Phenotype   Brown eyes
Genotype   BB or Bb

Phenotype   Blue eyes
Genotype   bb

Human characteristics

Dominant	Recessive
Wide nostrils	Narrow nostrils
Full lips	Thin lips
Dimples	No dimples
Early baldness in men	No early baldness
Freckles	No freckles
Dark hair	Light hair
Tongue rollers	Non-rollers
Normal pigmentation	Albinos
Dark skin	Fair skin
Free ear lobe	Ear lobe joined

Crosses

There are two easy ways of showing the results of crosses. One method uses lines and the other uses a punnet square. Both are shown below.

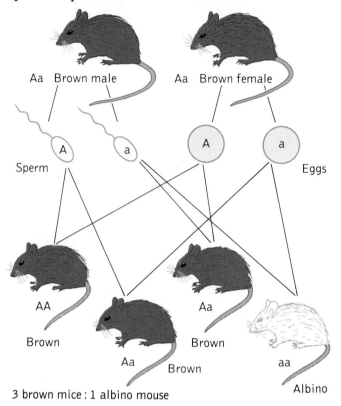

3 brown mice : 1 albino mouse

If both adults carry a recessive gene for the albino characteristic, there is a 1 in 4 chance that their young will be albinos.

Punnet square

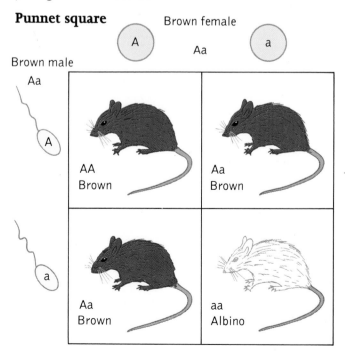

3 brown mice : 1 albino mouse

Co-dominance

In some cases both alleles affect the organism. This is called **co-dominance**. An example of this is found with blood groups. There are four different groups A, B, AB and O.

Group	A	B	AB	O
Genotype	AA or AO	BB or BO	AB	OO
Chemical produced in plasma	Anti-B	Anti-A	Anti-A Anti-B	None

A is dominant to O. B is dominant to O. A and B both have an effect so they are co-dominant.

It is important when people are given blood transfusions to give the correct group or clotting of the blood will occur.

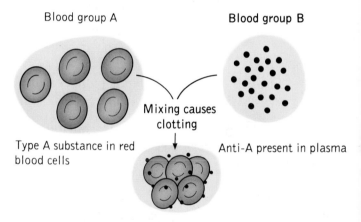

Blood group A · Blood group B
Mixing causes clotting
Type A substance in red blood cells · Anti-A present in plasma

Incomplete dominance

An example of incomplete dominance is shown by snapdragons: RR are red flowers, rr are white flowers, and Rr are pink. Probably two alleles are needed for the full development of the red colour.

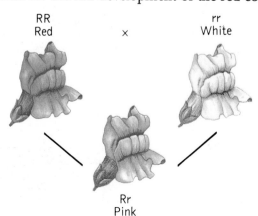

RR Red × rr White

Rr Pink

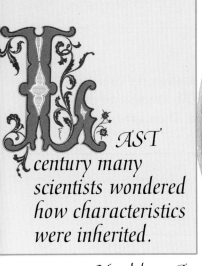

LAST century many scientists wondered how characteristics were inherited.

Mendel, an Austrian monk, was interested in breeding plants.

A

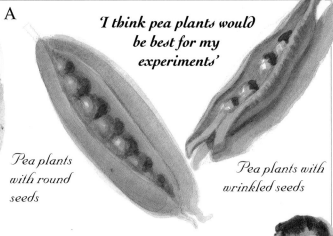

'I think pea plants would be best for my experiments'

Pea plants with round seeds

Pea plants with wrinkled seeds

'I will use these plants as the parents.'

B

Mendel transferred pollen from the plants producing round seeds to the plants producing wrinkled seeds.

'All the new seeds from my crosses must be planted and then we will have to wait.'

C

'That's strange! They are all round - not one wrinkled pea!

'I will plant all these round seeds, let them self-fertilize, and then see what happens.'

One year later . . .

D

5474 Round seeds
1850 Wrinkled seeds

'That's about 3 to 1 of round to wrinkled seeds.

'What next? - I suppose plant these round and wrinkled seeds.'

'Not more peas to plant!'

E

'The round seeds produce both round and wrinkled seeds. The wrinkled seeds are different - they only produce wrinkled seeds. I will call this recessive and the round shape dominant.'

6022 yellow
2001 green
3·01:1

787 tall
277 dwarf
2·5

'No questions! - Do they understand?'

Mendel died in 1884. In 1900, 35 years after his work was published, it was rediscovered and other scientists then realized its importance.

Mendel's peas

Mendel worked with pea plants because they were easy to grow and had clear-cut differences. Each flower of a pea plant contains both male and female sex cells. If left alone, these will fertilize themselves and produce seeds. But by taking pollen from one plant and brushing it on to the female parts of another plant, Mendel could cross-fertilize the plants to produce hybrids.

Mendel used other pairs of characteristics as well as round and wrinkled seeds. Each time, his results were the same. Mendel did not just look at his results, he counted them. This is probably why he was able to learn more from his experiments.

What were his results?

● In the first generation one characteristic only would show up.
● In the second generation, when the first generation was self-fertilized, the characteristic always appeared in a ratio of 3:1 cases.

He called the characteristic which showed in the first generation and more frequently in the second generation dominant. The other he called recessive.

How did he explain his results?

Mendel suggested that each plant must have two factors (now known as genes) for a characteristic.

If a plant received two dominant, or one dominant and one recessive factor, then it would show the dominant feature. Only if it received both in the recessive form would this characteristic show.

It was a pity that no one realized how important his work was at the time. Mendel had explained how characteristics were passed from one generation to the next but it was 35 years before his work was rediscovered and its importance realized.

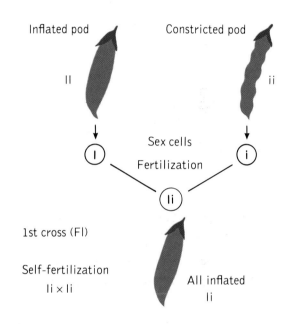

This would produce a ratio of 3 inflated pods to 1 constricted pod in the second generation (F2)

Mendel's results.

Character	Cross	Results of F2	Ratio
Seed shape	Round × wrinkled	5474 round, 1880 wrinkled	2.96:1
Pod shape	Inflated × constricted	882 inflated, 299 constricted	2.95:1
Stem length	Tall × dwarf	787 tall, 277 dwarf	2.84:1
Cotyledon	Yellow × green	6022 yellow, 2001 green	3.01:1
Flower	Axial × terminal	651 axial, 207 terminal	3.14:1

A In your own words explain how Mendel carried out this experiment with round and wrinkled seeds. Why did Mendel choose pea plants? What did his results show?

B Suggest some reasons why you think the importance of Mendel's work was not appreciated when it was first published.

C Draw diagrams to show the likely results of a similar cross between a different pair of characteristics:

a Tall(T) and dwarf(t) plants.
b Green(G) and yellow(g) pods.

Questions and activities

A Copy and complete this diagram to show the likely hair colour of this couple's children.

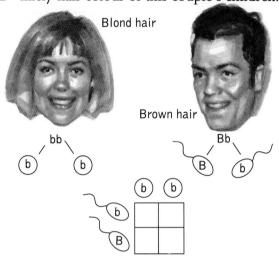

Blond hair

Brown hair

bb

b   b

Bb

B   b

b   b

b

B

From your diagram find examples of:

a a homozygote;
b a heterozygote;
c a phenotype;
d a genotype;
e a dominant gene;
f a recessive gene.

B Emma has curly hair with the genotype Cc. Her husband, Alex, has straight hair with the genotype cc. Draw a diagram like the one above to show what type of hair their children might inherit.

C Queen Victoria was a carrier for the disease haemophilia. With this disease the blood will not clot if a blood vessel is damaged. Explain why some of her children suffered from the disease while others were unaffected. Why does this disease only affect males?

Victoria   XX   Albert   XY

Gene for ———   ⌐— Normal gene
haemophilia

D Menna breeds cats. When she mated a black male with a white female all the young were black.

Explain why all the kittens were black.

E Look at the photographs of albinos on page 21. Explain how very occasionally an albino is produced in a population of different coloured animals. Would an albino give rise to a new population of white-coated animals?

F What would you expect the young to be like if you mated these cattle with mixed red and white hair? Show your results in diagrams.

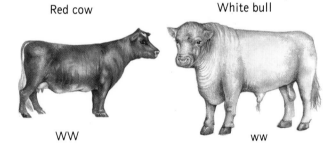

Red cow   White bull

WW   ww

Calves with red and white hair

Ww

G Dave and Steve both say they are the father of Ben. Ben belongs to blood group O and so does his mother. Dave is group A and Steve is AB. Only one of these men could have been Ben's father. Who is this? You will need to look at the information on blood groups in the *Factfile* to help you answer this question.

H In a family, the father has brown eyes and the mother has blue eyes. They have five children all with brown eyes. Is it possible for their next child to have blue eyes? Explain your answer.

The O'Sullivan family tree

Sean can.

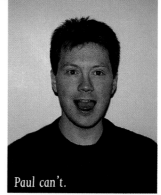

Paul can't.

Tongue roller

Non-roller

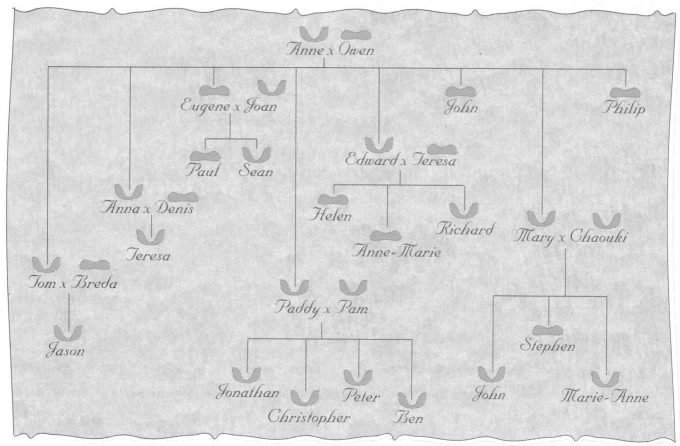

a The ability to roll your tongue is controlled by a single pair of genes. Study the family tree of the O'Sullivans and work out which gene is dominant, rolling or not rolling the tongue. How did you decide on your answer?

b Using R for the dominant gene and r for the recessive gene, redraw the family tree putting in the genotypes where you can work these out for certain.

c Complete the table for each person in the family tree.

Homozygous	Heterozygous	Not possible to decide

d If Paul marries a non-roller, what would you expect their children to be?

e You may be able to find variations controlled by genes in your family. It is important that they are not all the same for the characteristic you choose. One of the following may be suitable:

Eye colour (blue/non-blue)
Ear lobe (free/joined)
Tongue roller (can/cannot)

Produce a family tree for as many members of your family as you can. Remember to include, if possible, grandparents, parents, brothers, sisters, aunts, uncles, cousins. Use a symbol for the gene you have chosen. What can you learn about the feature from your family tree?

Hide and seek

Some animals hunt their prey. Other living things try to avoid being eaten. If they do this well, they are more likely to live and reproduce.

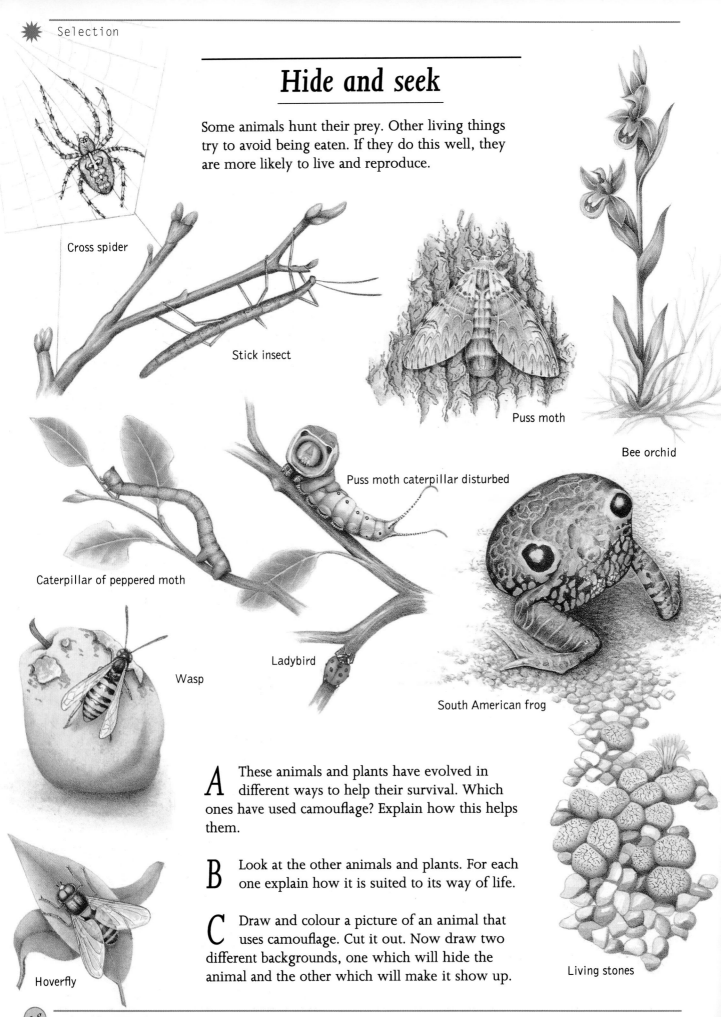

Cross spider

Stick insect

Puss moth

Bee orchid

Puss moth caterpillar disturbed

Caterpillar of peppered moth

Ladybird

South American frog

Wasp

Hoverfly

Living stones

A These animals and plants have evolved in different ways to help their survival. Which ones have used camouflage? Explain how this helps them.

B Look at the other animals and plants. For each one explain how it is suited to its way of life.

C Draw and colour a picture of an animal that uses camouflage. Cut it out. Now draw two different backgrounds, one which will hide the animal and the other which will make it show up.

Good breeding

Evolution takes place more quickly when we select features we like or need and breed them into domesticated animals and cultivated plants.

Wild daffodils.

A Every year new daffodils are produced by selecting and breeding. Make a list of the differences between the cultivated varieties and the wild daffodil.

B The same thing has happened with roses, dogs, cats, horses, cows, sheep, goldfish and many more. Choose one of these and collect pictures to make a display of the range of varieties.

C You are in charge of a breeding programme for an animal which is to be introduced as a new pet. Make a list of the features you think it should have.

Key facts: selection

● Only those organisms best suited to their environment will survive.

● We can improve the types of crops and cattle by selective breeding.

● New types of plants can be grown more quickly by cuttings or tissue culture.

● Gene mutations may provide improved features.

Struggle for existence

These female land crabs each carry 100 000 eggs. Only a few will survive to become adults.

All organisms produce far more offspring than are needed for the survival of the species. Most of the young die at a very early stage either from lack of food, predation, an unsuitable climate or disease. Since many young will die, there will be a struggle for existence. Young plants which grow faster and have stronger roots will be the ones to survive.

Natural selection

Those forms best suited to their environment are the ones that survive. This is often referred to as 'survival of the fittest'. If a mutation gives a better chance of survival then this will be passed on to new generations. In this way new kinds of organisms can arise. Those predators that are best at finding or hunting prey will be more likely to get food. Prey better hidden, faster moving or poisonous will avoid being eaten.

This pink crab spider can lie in wait undetected.

An example of natural selection

The peppered moth is a good example of this. The normal form is speckled grey and white. This is well camouflaged against the lichen-covered bark of trees. During the last century a black mutant appeared. Many trees and buildings were sooty due to the industrial revolution. The light form of the moth was no longer camouflaged and its numbers decreased but the black form became more common. The Clean Air Act resulted in less soot deposits and from 1956 the numbers of the light forms in towns have increased.

Tissue culture

New plants can be produced by growing a few cells into a complete specimen.

In this way many new plants can be produced very quickly with the required features.

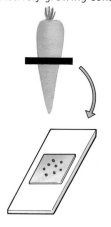

Actively growing cells

Placed in culture medium

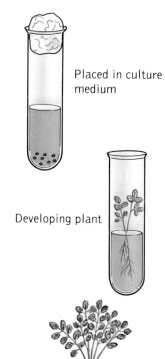

Developing plant

Full flowering plant

Selective breeding

We have bred plants and animals for thousands of years to improve their usefulness.

For example:

● pigs which put on weight faster;
● sheep with more wool;
● cereals with more grain;
● disease-resistant plants;
● plants with bigger and brighter petals.

These sheep have been bred to produce more wool.

We look for those features which are most useful in the parent plants or animals. We then breed from these to obtain young with the desired characteristics.

Cuttings

Some plants can be increased by taking cuttings, e.g. roses, geraniums, or by growing bulbs, tubers, runners, etc. These new plants or **clones** will have the same genes as their parent plant. This can be used commercially to grow large numbers of plants with desirable features.

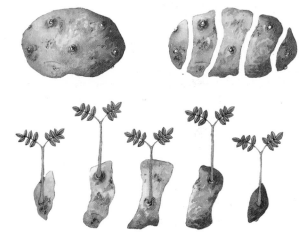

New plants identical to parent

Finding new mutants

If a plant breeder cannot find the required genes in a parent then it may be possible to make new ones. A variety of agents can cause genes to mutate. These include X-rays, gamma rays, ultraviolet light and some chemicals. The plants are exposed to one of these and a new mutated gene which produces a changed characteristic may occur.

This technique has been used to produce barley that is resistant to mildew, bacteria that produce higher yields of antibiotics, and in 1950 a new rice variety that would grow in cooler climates.

Very occasionally plants produce 'sports' or mutants.

Darwin's theory of natural selection

Most scientists believe that the living things we see today have descended from forms which lived many years ago. Charles Darwin was the first person to put forward this theory. In the 1830s Darwin sailed round the world in a ship called the *Beagle*. He visited many countries studying and collecting information about all the different animals he found.

After visiting the mainland of South America, he sailed 970 km to the Galapagos Islands. These islands have risen from the sea due to volcanic action and have only been in existence for about 2 million years. Darwin was intrigued by the different animals he found on the islands. He wondered where they had come from. Why did each island have a different type of giant tortoise? Why were there different finches on the islands? He had not found the same animals anywhere else.

On the mainland he had found a lizard or iguana which lived in trees and ate leaves. On one of the islands a similar iguana lived on rocks and dived into the sea to feed on seaweed. Had the iguana been carried on a dead tree from the mainland to the island? Perhaps they had then changed to suit the different conditions on the island. After many years they had become so changed that they were now a new species.

A marine iguana from the Galapagos Islands.

1. Geospiza magnirostris. 2. Geospiza fortis.
3. Geospiza parvula. 4. Certhidea olivacea.

FINCHES FROM GALAPAGOS ARCHIPELAGO.

These ideas became the basis of Darwin's theory of natural selection or 'survival of the fittest'. After many more years of research, Darwin published his theories in 1859 in a book called *On the Origin of Species*. It contained the following main points:

● Animals and plants produce far more young than are needed for the organism to survive.
● All species show variations.
● Varieties most suited to their environment will be the ones to survive and reproduce.
● The favourable characteristics will be passed to their offspring.

Many people did not like Darwin's theory. It suggested that humans had evolved from some ape-like ancestor. This was regarded as ridiculous by most people and there were many jokes about his theory. Now, much more evidence exists to support the theory and his ideas are believed by most scientists.

Cloning

A major problem for plant breeders is time. Selective breeding programmes can take many years to produce new useful plants. However cloning by tissue culture methods has meant that for some plants large numbers can be produced far more quickly.

It has not been possible to develop the same technique with animal tissue yet. However recent research suggests it will be possible to produce large numbers of genetically identical animals by a different method.

Nuclei are removed from some tadpole cells all with the same genes. The nuclei in frogs' eggs are then destroyed and the new nuclei introduced. These will then develop into tadpoles with the same genes. In time it will be possible to take cells from a cow with a very high milk yield and by cloning produce a new herd all able to produce the same high milk yields.

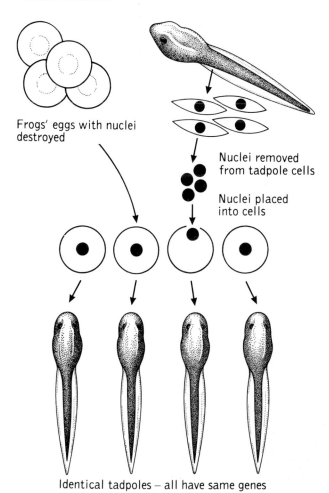

Frogs' eggs with nuclei destroyed

Nuclei removed from tadpole cells

Nuclei placed into cells

Identical tadpoles – all have same genes

A Find the Galapogos Islands in an atlas. Draw a map of these and show some of the different animals found on these islands. You will need to find library books to help you.

B Give possible reasons for each of the following:

a Darwin found many different species of animals on the mainland of South America but only a few on each of the Galapogos Islands.
b Tourists who visit the Galapogos Islands have been surprised to find that the animals show no fear of people.
c Each island has different types of finches with different shaped beaks.

C If we could clone cows it would also be possible to clone people. Discuss in groups why you think anyone might want to produce lots of identical people. Make a list of possible advantages and dangers of cloning people. Would you pass a law banning this? Why?

D Professor Makemor has developed a technique for cloning people. Write a story about the problems that occur when he produces a hundred identical people.

Questions and activities

A Rewrite this passage choosing the correct word from each pair. Mutations occur by chance/planning. Usually these are harmful/beneficial. Living things produce more/fewer offspring than are needed and the majority will live/die. Natural/Artificial selection will favour the survival of those organisms most/least suited to their environment.

B You may have read an adventure story called *The Black Tulip* by Alexander Dumas about trying to breed a black tulip. Make up your own story about a person who tries to breed a new animal or plant. What kinds of problems might arise? Make sure you do some research to make your story seem realistic.

C A major problem with the natural selection of mutants is that it may favour some organisms which you do not want. This happened in hospitals in the 1940s when they began to make wide use of the antibiotic, penicillin. Any mutant strains of bacteria causing diseases which were less affected by penicillin survived and were able to infect patients.

Results from one hospital

Date	Total number of patients	Patients with penicillin-resistant strains
Apr.–Nov. 1946	99	15
Feb.–Jun. 1947	100	38
Feb.–Jun. 1948	100	59

a What do you think would have happened over the next few years to the numbers of resistant forms?
b What are the major problems caused by the selection of these new strains?
c Why do you think it happened more quickly in hospitals than anywhere else?

D Rats are a serious problem. They spread disease and damage stored food crops. In the 1950s, the poison Warfarin killed the rats by interfering with blood clotting. In 1958 some rats caught near Glasgow were found to be resistant to Warfarin. Their blood was not affected by Warfarin. By 1972, 12 areas in Britain were known to have Warfarin-resistant rats. Warfarin resistance is thought to be determined by a single dominant gene.

a Plan an investigation that could be carried out to find out if Warfarin resistance is controlled by a single dominant gene.
b Would you expect that, in time, all rats in this country will become resistant to Warfarin?
c What advice could be offered now about the control of rats?

E Whole plants can now be grown from pollen grains. The plants grown from these have cells with single sets of chromosomes: they are haploid plants. If the pollen grains are treated with a chemical the chromosomes will double, producing diploid plants.

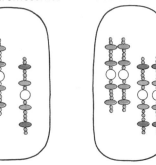

Cell of plant showing two pairs of chromosomes

Pollen grain with single set of chromosomes

Haploid plant one set of chromosomes

Diploid plant two sets of chromosomes

The haploid plants are sterile but the diploid plants will breed normally.

a How are these plants different from those grown by tissue culture?
b Why are the haploid plants sterile?
c What would be the advantages of this method of culture?

Long-legged waders

Wading birds feed on small animals found in the mud at the edges of rivers or on mud flats in estuaries and bays. They have long legs to keep their feathers clear of the water. The leg length of any species will show some variation.

Wading birds need long legs to keep their feathers dry.

This population will not change unless the environment changes. Imagine the sea level increases by 1 cm each year.

a Draw a graph of the expected change in the population after 10 years.
b Describe, according to Darwin's ideas, how this change in the population would occur.
c How would you account for a new population of birds with much longer legs, say 40 cm?

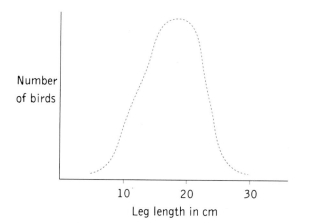

Number of birds

Leg length in cm

10   20   30

Genetic engineering

In recent years scientists have found ways of changing living things by inserting different genes.

A Make a list of the living things shown in this scene. For each one suggest some changes that you think would be for the better.

B Decide which changes in your list may be useful to humans. Would any of the changes harm the animals and plants?

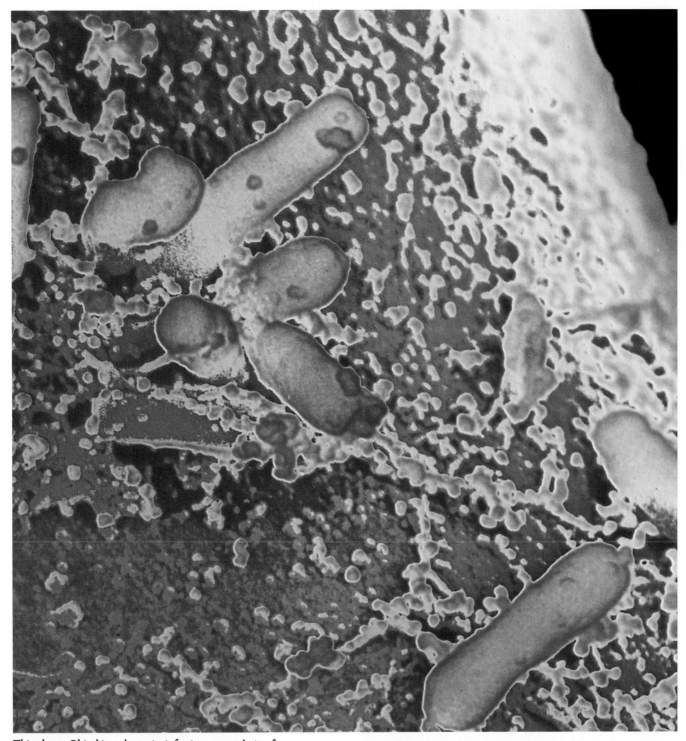

This shows Rhizobium bacteria infecting a root hair of a pea plant.

Some bacteria are able to convert nitrogen from the air into nitrates. It may be possible to insert the gene for fixing nitrogen into the roots of crops so that they will be able to make their own nitrates. This would avoid farmers using large quantities of expensive fertilizers to supply the nitrates needed for plant growth.

A Make a list of the advantages of introducing this gene into crops. Can you think of any harmful effects that may occur?

B By using the techniques of genetic engineering, it may be possible to create a new organism for feeding the human population. What features do you think it should have? Draw a large picture of your design with notes describing its main characteristics.

Key facts: genetic engineering

● New genes can be put into bacteria, plants and animals, including human beings, changing their characteristics.
● These new genes could:
> cure inherited diseases;
> make crops grow faster;
> give resistance to disease;
> make missing hormones;
> break down plastics; and
> make fuels.
● Viruses can carry the changed genes into cells.
● Bacteria can become chemical factories making large quantities of new drugs.

Changing living things

Amazing developments during the last few years have opened up exciting possibilities. Genes can be put into plants and animals changing their characteristics. Research is taking place to insert genes into chickens giving them resistance to many diseases. Similar developments are taking place with disease resistance in other animals and plants. New genes are being isolated that will increase the growth rates of crops, poultry and cattle. Many other ways will be found in the future to make use of these new techniques to change the characteristics of living things.

How genes are inserted

Viruses cause harmful diseases such as measles, influenza and AIDS. Surprisingly they may also become important in helping to cure diseases. They can damage human tissues because they are able to penetrate cells. This ability may well be put to good use. A cell makes its own protein. When a virus enters, it changes the normal action of the cell so that virus protein is made. A virus with a changed gene will cause the cell to make new proteins from the new instructions it receives. In this way it is possible to place a useful gene into a virus which can carry the new gene into a cell and change its action.

The carrier viruses are changed so that they will not reproduce and infect new animals or plants with the changed genes. If viruses with altered genes were able to reproduce and infect new organisms it could lead to serious problems. Imagine a gene for breaking down plastics spreading into the environment. This could create havoc in the wrong places.

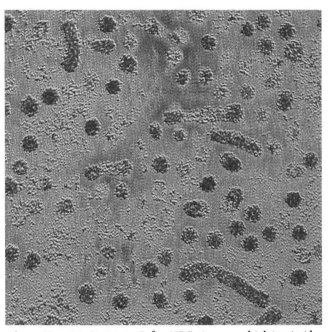

Above: Hepatitis B viruses. Left: AIDS viruses multiplying inside an infected cell. Some viruses may have a useful role carrying genes into living things.

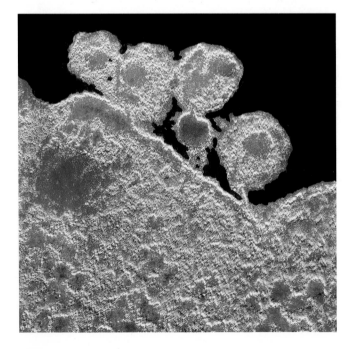

A cure for inherited diseases?

This research may be of great importance to humans in finding cures to various diseases. One in 2000 children in the UK is born with the disease cystic fibrosis. An abnormal gene causes cells in their lungs to produce large quantities of thick mucus. This blocks the air passages and makes bacterial infections more likely. At present there is no cure.

Scientists are now developing ways of introducing the normal gene into their lung cells so that they will behave normally. They have already been able to do this with cells grown in the laboratory from a person suffering from cystic fibrosis. Inserting normal genes into the cells has corrected the problem. Maybe as a result of genetic engineering, cystic fibrosis will become a disease of the past.

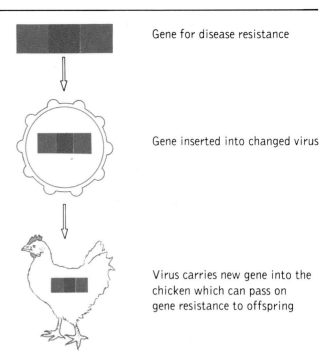

Gene for disease resistance

Gene inserted into changed virus

Virus carries new gene into the chicken which can pass on gene resistance to offspring

Release of 'supercrops'

The first crops produced commercially are now to be grown outside the laboratory. These 'supercrops' have genes added to make them resistant to herbicides. When the fields are sprayed with weed-killers only the crops will survive. But there are fears the genes could lead to undesirable features or spread to other plants. There are also plans to release plants which can produce their own natural insecticides. Could this have dangerous consequences for the world's insect life?

Other plans for the future

Every week new suggestions are made for possible developments in gene transfer. Scientists are trying to produce new microbes that will break down oil. These could be used to treat oil slicks thus avoiding pollution of water. Other microbes could be developed to change waste plastics and paper into a useful fuel. In Brazil, sugar cane is used to make alcohol. This is used as a fuel for motor cars. Perhaps the genes for producing alcohol could be inserted into the sugar cane so that the fuel is made by the plant. The possibilities seem endless.

Bacteria as chemical factories

Genes can be inserted into bacteria making them produce different chemicals, e.g. vaccines, antibiotics or hormones. Because bacteria divide quickly to form large colonies, it is possible to use them to make chemicals in large quantities. As the bacteria divide they will pass on the new instructions to all the cells in the colony.

These bacteria, E. coli, grow inside the human intestine where they divide at a very rapid rate. One individual can produce 2×10^{10} bacteria per day.

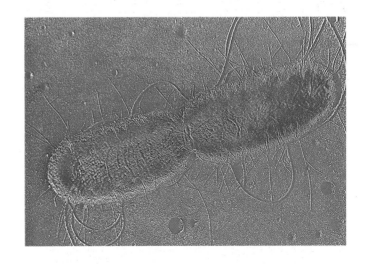

Making use of genes

Genetic engineering is one of the most exciting developments of modern science. It could lead to many new ways of fighting disease, increasing food supplies and dealing with problems of waste. However, it may hold hidden dangers which need to be understood before these new techniques are used on a large scale.

Making insulin

Insulin controls the amount of sugar in the blood. Some people suffer from a disease called diabetes mellitus when their pancreas stops making insulin. This disease used to be very serious but can now be controlled by injections of insulin. This is extracted from the pancreas of animals but is expensive to make as large numbers of pancreases are needed. This animal insulin is slightly different from human insulin and can cause unpleasant side effects. Now, with genetic engineering, scientists have discovered a new, cheaper way of making insulin. The human gene for making this hormone has been extracted from the pancreas cells and put into bacterial cells. These cells divide many times to produce large colonies of bacterial cells able to make human insulin. Unfortunately, some people have not found this new insulin effective. More research is needed before all diabetics can benefit from its use.

A substitute for blood

In 1991 it was announced that American scientists have succeeded in producing human haemoglobin from pigs. Haemoglobin is the chemical in red blood cells which carries oxygen round the body. If

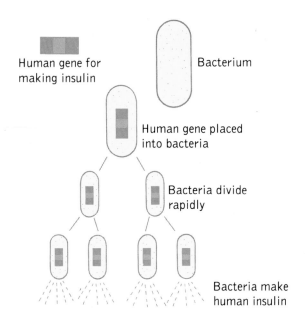

Human gene for making insulin

Bacterium

Human gene placed into bacteria

Bacteria divide rapidly

Bacteria make human insulin

this could be made easily it would avoid the need for costly blood transfusions. The human haemoglobin would have to be separated from the remainder of the pig's blood to avoid passing on any harmful substances.

Copies of the human gene for making haemoglobin were injected into day-old pig embryos. These were then placed into adult female pigs. The new piglets when born were found to have about 15% of human haemoglobin in their blood. With further research they hope to increase this amount. It was claimed that a blood substitute would have saved the lives of 10 000 soldiers on the battlefields of Vietnam where blood for transfusions was not available.

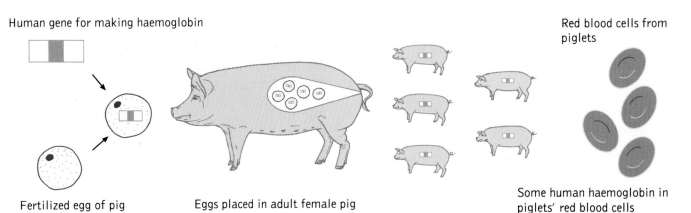

Human gene for making haemoglobin

Fertilized egg of pig

Eggs placed in adult female pig

Red blood cells from piglets

Some human haemoglobin in piglets' red blood cells

A cure for cancer?

Another development may help in the cure of cancer. A gene has been identified that causes the production of a chemical, TNF, which attacks cancer cells. It is planned to use a virus to carry this gene into white blood cells removed from the patient. These will then be increased in number in the laboratory before being replaced in the patient. These cells, now able to produce TNF, are expected to move towards the tumour and attack the cancer cells.

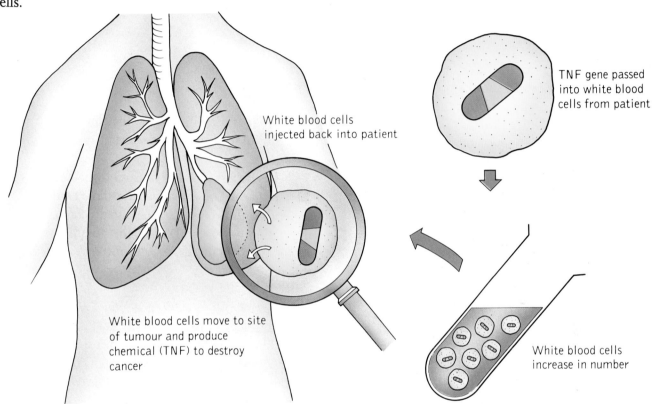

Virus carries TNF gene

TNF gene passed into white blood cells from patient

White blood cells injected back into patient

White blood cells move to site of tumour and produce chemical (TNF) to destroy cancer

White blood cells increase in number

The hidden dangers

Though genetic engineering holds great promise, it also poses many problems. We have to consider whether it is right to alter the genetic make-up of any living things. No doubt we would all agree it should be used to cure serious diseases affecting many people, but should we use it to make people stronger, taller, more intelligent?

What would happen if a changed gene escaped into the environment? Suppose a gene had been developed to help new cells grow after an injury. If this spread to more people it could cause a major epidemic of cancers. Scientists have to obtain permission before any changed genes are used outside the laboratory because it is thought that the effects are difficult to predict and may lead to major disasters.

● There is enormous concern that although this latest research could be very important in fighting disease, it could also have disastrous effects. Many experiments have been banned because of the dangers of introducing changed genes into the environment.

a Discuss in groups the possible advantages and disadvantages of genetic engineering.

b Make a list of reasons to support this type of research and reasons for banning its continuation.

Questions and activities

A Use words from the word list to complete this passage. They may be used more than once or not at all.

viruses   **bacteria**   **genes**   **food supply**

life   **slowly**   **quickly**   **vitamins**   **hormones**

With genetic engineering scientists can change living things. _____ from one organism can be transferred to another. This means there are new ways of improving our _____, fighting disease and making chemicals in short supply. Humans need a supply of certain vitamins that we cannot make. These _____ are made by other animals and plants. Perhaps it will be possible to transfer the _____ for making these vitamins into humans so that we can make them for ourselves. Or these genes could be inserted into _____. As the bacteria divide, _____, they would be able to make large quantities of vitamins, _____, vaccines and other useful chemicals.

B Some people never grow to adult height. This disease can be cured by giving injections of a growth hormone, pituitrin, during childhood. However this growth hormone is in very short supply and it has not been possible to treat all children with the disease. Now with genetic engineering the hormone can be produced far more easily. Write an article with diagrams explaining how this hormone can be produced in sufficient quantities for all those requiring treatment.

Perhaps with genetic engineering these pictures will only be found in history books.

C This chart has been started for you. Make a large copy and then find examples from this section to complete it.

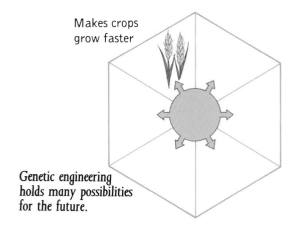

Makes crops grow faster

Genetic engineering holds many possibilities for the future.

D What is it about viruses that makes them useful to genetic engineers?

E Researchers have produced tomatoes that take twice as long to ripen as ordinary ones. This depends on introducing a changed gene that affects the ripening process. Discuss the possible advantages and disadvantages of the wider use of this gene.

F Some young children in developing countries suffer from Kwashiorkor. This is a disease caused by a diet lacking sufficient protein. The food most readily available to them is cereal. These plants contain protein but they lack the correct types and proportions of amino acids needed by humans. Animal proteins are more useful for humans. Describe how genetic engineering could change the cereal to produce an ideal balanced diet to help solve the world's malnutrition problems.

G The scientists working on the ways in which gene transfer may be used to cure cancers have stressed that the genes will work only in the patient's body; they cannot be inherited by any future offspring; and they cannot be passed to any other person. Why is this important?

H By the time you read this book there will have been more developments by genetic engineers. Make a collection of articles on this topic from newspapers and magazines. Write your own *Factfile* box with details of the latest ways in which gene transfer is being used.

A fishy problem!

For many years salmon has been an expensive food. More recently it has become one of the cheaper forms of animal protein available in our shops. It is now being farmed in large numbers around the estuaries of Scotland. It may be possible to make the salmon grow faster as scientists are working on a gene that produces growth hormones in fish. Should it be used?

People have been interviewed to find out their views.

John East, a fish farmer

"It has made a big difference to this area. There is more work for everyone. Anything which will make the fish grow more quickly will mean we can sell more and employ more people. Very few fish escape into the wild so I don't think that would be a problem. I think we should use this new gene."

Professor of Environmental Hazards, Bedton University

"Some fish kept on fish farms are bound to escape. These will be likely to breed with the wild salmon and pass on the changed genes. We do not know what effect this could have on the fish population. It may prevent normal growth of the salmon and cause a serious decline in the wild population. It could be passed on to other species of fish with disastrous consequences. We do not know enough about the possible effects."

Flora Dipil, nutritionist

"Salmon is a very good food. It is much lower in saturated fats than meat. If people changed their diet to have more fish they would be less likely to get heart disease."

Reverend Mary Wise

"I do not believe anyone has the right to change living things. They were not created by man. We should preserve the wildlife that we have on this planet, not change it purely to suit our needs."

Maggie McBrane, mother of six

"We eat salmon quite often now, it is so much cheaper. If they can grow the fish more quickly it would be even cheaper and we would eat salmon at least once a week."

I. Hookam, fisherman

"Fishing is my main hobby. I spend most weekends and my holidays fishing for salmon. I would be very concerned if these changed salmon escaped and bred with the wild salmon. Who knows what harm these new genes would do! If they were intended to grow more quicky they would have the gene already."

Dr Jean Master

"We have been trying out these new genes on fish in captivity. We add the new gene to the eggs and then grow the fish in tanks. In some cases fish have grown 20 times faster. We could make the fish sterile although this would mean having to treat each new batch of eggs to insert the gene. If we did not make the fish sterile then future generations of fish would inherit the new gene."

> You have been asked to consider the problem and decide what should happen.
>
> ● Work in small groups. Discuss the views expressed by the different people.
>
> ● Write a brief report of your recommendations explaining why you have made your decisions.

The variety of life

All living things can be divided into groups of animals or plants with similar features. This chart shows the major groups of living things.

Large groups can be subdivided further. The arthropods are shown as an example.

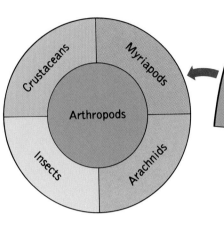

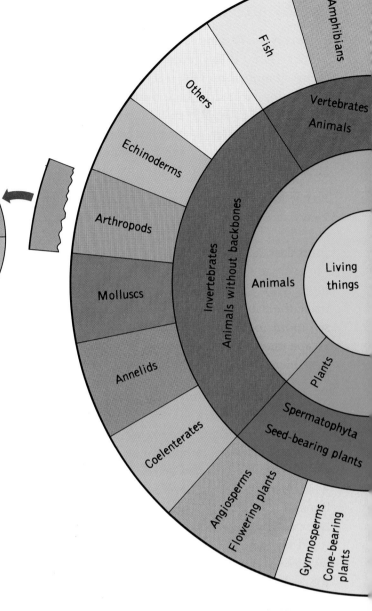

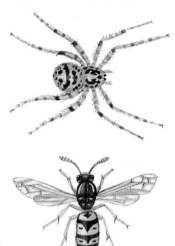

Crustaceans Hard exoskeleton. Head and thorax fused. Two pairs of antennae, gills, many jointed legs.

Myriapods Many legs, 1 pair of antennae. Millipedes: 2 pairs of legs per segment. Centipedes: 1 pair of legs per segment.

Arachnids Two main body regions. Four pairs of legs. No antennae.

Insects Head, thorax and abdomen. Strengthened exoskeleton. One pair of antennae, 3 pairs of legs, tracheal system; 0, 1 or 2 pairs of wings.

A Complete the table showing characteristics of vertebrates. The first one has been filled in to help you.

Class	Skin	Warm-blooded	Eggs or live young	Oxygen uptake	Care of young
Birds	Feathers	Yes	Eggs	Lungs	Incubates eggs, feeds young

B Look at the chart showing the subdivision of arthropods. Produce a similar chart for one of the following groups: reptiles, mammals, fish, molluscs, fungi, algae.

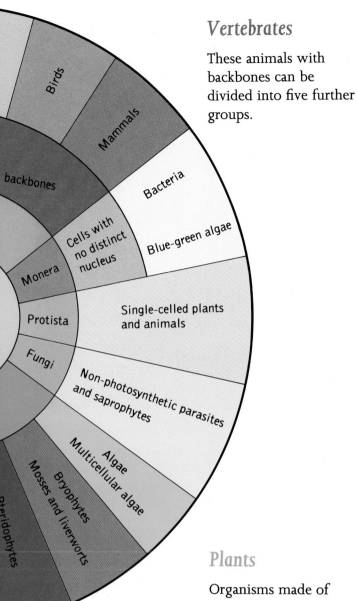

Vertebrates

These animals with backbones can be divided into five further groups.

Fish Streamlined body, gills, scales, fins. External fertilization. Soft-shelled eggs laid in water.

Amphibians Tadpole stage lives in water. Smooth, moist skin. External fertilization of soft-shelled eggs. Adults have lungs.

Reptiles Dry, scaly skin. No tadpole stage. Lungs. Internal fertilization. Eggs with hard shell laid on land.

Birds Control body temperature (warm-blooded). Feathers, beak, wings. Internal fertilization. Hard-shelled eggs incubated by parents. Young fed by parents.

Mammals Control body temperature (warm-blooded). Hairy skin, diaphragm. Internal fertilization. Young develop inside uterus. Fed with milk produced in mammary glands.

Plants

Organisms made of many cells containing the green pigment chlorophyll. They make their own food by photosynthesis.

Algae Simple plants like seaweeds without roots, stems or leaves. Live in water.

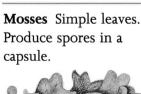

Mosses Simple leaves. Produce spores in a capsule.

Fungi Not true plants as they cannot photosynthesize. Live on dead plants or on living organisms. Made from fine interwoven threads.

Ferns Roots, stems and leaves. Spores found on underside of leaves.

Flowering plants Roots, stems and leaves. Many types like buttercups to oak trees. Produce seeds in a fruit.

The genetic code

Genes are made of DNA, deoxyribonucleic acid. Watson and Crick, working in Cambridge in 1953, discovered the structure of this important chemical. It controls the characteristics in all living things. The genetic code consists of different arrangements of four bases:

Adenine A
Thymine T
Cytosine C
Guanine G

It is like a code made of four letters. All plants and animals use the same code and yet the different arrangements of these four bases are responsible for all the different features found in living things. It seems impossible but it works!

DNA has a shape like a twisted ladder, called a *double helix*, where the rungs are the four bases. Adenine (A) always pairs with thymine (T) and cytosine (C) always pairs with guanine (G).

Making more DNA

When cells divide the chromosomes have to duplicate themselves. They need to make exact copies. The DNA unzips itself and free bases take up their positions to form new strands of DNA. This process of copying is called **replication**. In this way the cell can make new identical chromosomes after division.

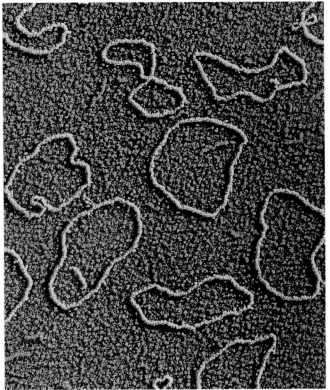

DNA from the bacterium *Escherichia coli*.

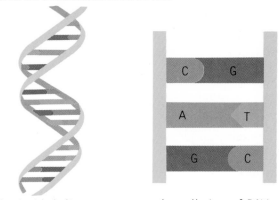

The double helix

A small piece of DNA

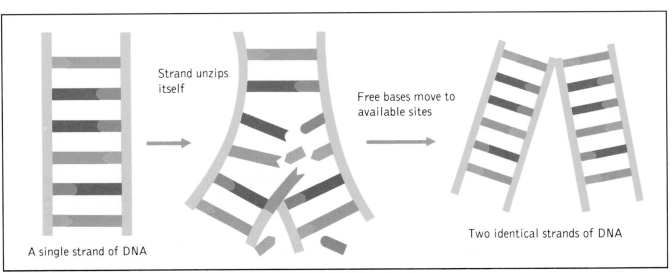

Strand unzips itself

Free bases move to available sites

A single strand of DNA

Two identical strands of DNA

Replication of DNA.

Making proteins

Genes work by making different proteins. **Enzymes** are proteins that cause chemical reactions. For instance, a gene in some plants will cause an enzyme to be produced which makes the red colour in petals:

red colour in petals

↑

enzyme

↑

gene

The genes are in the nucleus of a cell but the proteins are made in the cytoplasm. A chemical called **messenger RNA** (mRNA) makes a copy of a length of DNA or one gene. This smaller molecule can pass through the nuclear membrane and acts as a code to determine the sequence of amino acids in the protein. Different proteins or enzymes have different arrangements of amino acids.

Each of the 20 naturally occurring amino acids has a group of three bases which will attach themselves to the messenger RNA. In this way the RNA will determine the sequence of amino acids in the protein.

Mutations

A change of one base in the DNA will change the RNA and therefore the sequence of amino acids in the protein. An example of this is found in a serious disease, sickle-celled anaemia. A change in a single DNA base causes a change in the enzyme responsible for making haemoglobin. This chemical carries oxygen in the blood but when altered it no longer works properly.

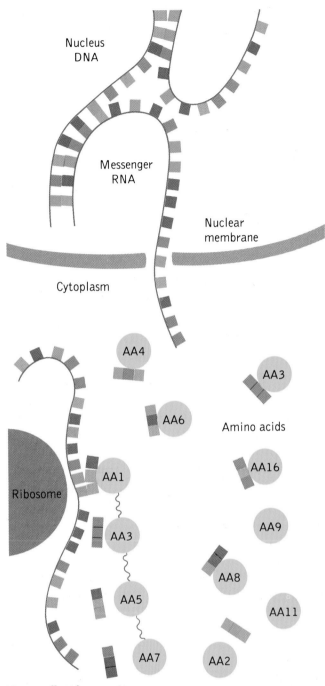

How a cell makes proteins.

A Use different coloured plastic-covered wires to make a number of chromosome pairs. Use these to show what happens at cell division and when DNA replicates itself.

B Produce a flow chart of the stages in making proteins.

C Study the diagrams showing the amino acids forming the protein chain. Which amino acids will be added next? Complete the chain:

AA7–AA5–AA3–AA1–?–?–?

D Using card and coloured sticky paper make a model to explain how DNA controls protein synthesis.

The origin of our species

Where did the first person come from? How did our species *Homo sapiens* come into being? The theory of evolution suggests that we are descended from earlier animals. Fossils of our ancestors have given us some clues, but fossils are hard to find and we are still a long way from knowing the full story.

The fossils are too few for us to be sure when and where the first people lived. From the information we can piece together, we have a picture of our ancestors gradually walking upright and becoming more intelligent, slowly building up the skills which we have today.

About 30 million years ago, in Africa, there lived a small creature called *Proconsul*. *Proconsul* lived on the ground, and walked on four legs. From *Proconsul* came two great families. One took to living in the trees of the African forest and developed into apes such as gorillas and chimpanzees. The other family, the *Hominids*, began to develop into human beings. East African fossils from between 2 and 4 million years ago show us much more human-like creatures called *Australopithecus africanus*. They were only about 1.2 m tall, but they walked upright and knew how to use stones as simple tools.

Starting about 2 million years ago we find fossils of *Homo habilis* and then *Homo erectus*. These were the first members of the genus *Homo*. Their brains were over half the size of ours, and they lived in camps of

Proconsul.

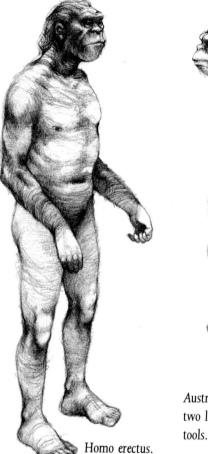

Homo erectus.

Australopithecus – walking on two legs frees hands to use tools.

Art – 20 000 years BC.

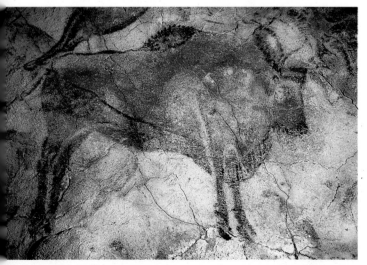

little huts they built. They were nearly as tall as us, and we find their remains in Europe and Asia as well as Africa.

Sometime over 1 million years ago, true people like ourselves appeared. They made good stone tools, used fire, and soon learned to paint pictures on the walls of their caves. They even buried their dead, so perhaps they had become religious. They were the first *Homo sapiens* (which means 'wise man').

Creation and evolution

Charles Darwin formed his ideas on evolution only about 150 years ago. His famous voyage of discovery on *The Beagle* began in 1831, and his book *On the Origin of Species* was published in 1859. Before that, the ideas most people had about their own origins came from their religion. In Europe, people took the account of the Creation in the Bible quite literally. God had made everything in six days. Every living thing was created separately. Adam and Eve, the first people, were made on the sixth day. On the seventh day God rested. Islam also clearly stated that people were made by God. The idea that we had descended from primitive animals was very shocking. Darwin's theories seemed to suggest that the Bible was wrong.

The young Charles Darwin . . .

. . . and as others saw him!

In our time the argument is still not over. People hold many different views on the subject:

● Some people believe that the theory of evolution means that there is no need to think about God when trying to decide where we came from.
● Others say that Darwin must have been wrong. They point out that evolution is only a theory, and that the evidence for it is not complete.
● Some religious people are quite happy to accept Darwin's ideas. They feel that evolution may have been the way that God used to create human beings. Darwin himself mentions the Creator in the final sentence of his book.

The Bible
Genesis, Chapter 2
God fashioned man of dust from the soil. Then he breathed into his nostrils a breath of life, and thus man became a living being.

The Qur'an
Sura 11, verse 61
He caused you to grow from the Earth.
Sura 6, verse 2
God is the One who fashioned you from clay.

The Bishop of Oxford
(arguing with T. H. Huxley, a supporter of Darwin, in 1860)
Is it through your grandmother or your grandfather that you claim to be descended from the apes?

On the Origin of Species
Final sentence
There is grandeur in this view of life . . . originally breathed by the Creator . . . from so simple a beginning endless forms most beautiful and wonderful have been and are being evolved.

A Think about our early ancestors, collecting fruit, hunting and fishing, bringing up children. They became taller and more intelligent. They began to walk on two legs. They lost their hairy coats.

How would each of these changes help them to survive? Remember to think about the survival of men *and* women.

B Which people could you talk to about the origin of human beings? Your science teacher? Your RE teacher? Parents? People where you worship? Ask their opinions, to help build up your own view.

How do new species separate?

Darwin's theory of evolution gives us an idea about the way new species are formed from older ones. Tiny changes build up over time until they add up to a completely new species. If this is true, we ought to be able to find examples in the world of this happening. Remember that evolution is not just something that happened millions of years ago. It is a continual process that will go on creating new species now and in the future.

Unfortunately evolution is a very slow thing, and so we cannot set up experiments to make it happen

whenever we want. Collecting experimental evidence for evolution is very difficult. However we can study the natural world and see if there are any signs of new species forming.

Gulls – new species in the making?

If we look at the different types of gulls living in the countries around the North Pole we can see a lot of variation. The gulls in different countries have different coloured wings, backs and legs.

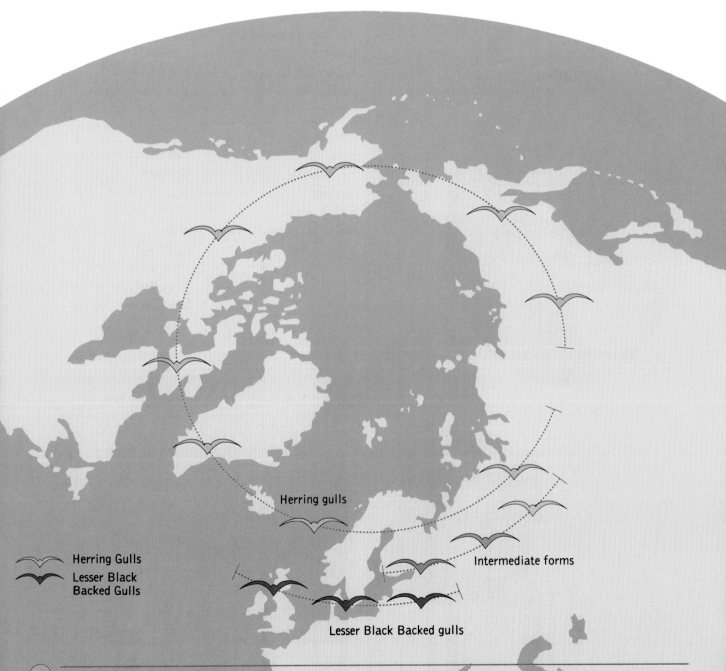

Herring gulls

Intermediate forms

Herring Gulls
Lesser Black
Backed Gulls

Lesser Black Backed gulls

The British gulls

In Britain we have two main types of gull. The Herring Gull has a pale grey back and wings and pink legs. The Lesser Black Backed Gull has a darker back and wings, and yellow legs. As well as looking quite different the two types do not breed together, so we classify them as two different species.

A journey around the world

This division into two species is not so easy as it looks. Imagine we are taking a journey around the world, starting in Britain and travelling west. You can follow this journey on the map. As we move into America we find Herring Gulls very similar to the British ones. Passing through Siberia and into Finland we find that the gulls are getting darker, and many start to have yellow legs. By the time we reach Britain again they have become the other type of British gull – the Lesser Black Backed!

The interesting question is, where does one species start and the other end? There just does not seem to be an answer. They merge into each other smoothly all around the world. Each type can breed with its neighbours, so in that sense they should all be counted as members of the *same* species. However the ones at the beginning and end of the range of variation, which both live in Britain, do not breed, so they must be *different* species.

An explanation

The theory of evolution explains this by saying that we have found a species which is in the middle of dividing into two. Not very long ago there was only one variety which has spread around the world, altering as it went. In Britain the extreme types have met again, but have become so different that they cannot breed.

The Lesser Black Backed Gull, Larus fuscus.

The Herring Gull, Larus argentatus.

A Suppose the gulls in Siberia died out.

a What kind of event might make this happen?
b How would that alter our view of the groups of gulls?

B A species showing gradual adaptive changes over a wide area is called **a cline**. Gulls form a cline.

a In what ways is mankind, *Homo sapiens*, a species which forms a cline?
b What main adaptations have we made to different climates?
c Unlike gulls, man's cline has not split. We all belong to the same species. What piece of evidence proves this statement?

Nature versus nurture?

It can be difficult to decide whether characteristics of living things are due to genetic make-up or the environment. Tongue rolling is obviously inherited but what about characteristics such as intelligence, musical ability or athletic excellence? Does a football star play well because he inherited certain genes or because he practised and trained hard? Is this ability due to one cause only or could it be a result of both genetic *and* environmental factors? Let us look at some of the evidence.

Did he inherit this ability?

Colour of Siamese cats

Siamese cats have an enzyme responsible for the development of the dark colour in the ears, paws and tail. This enzyme stops working at normal body temperature. For this reason only the cooler parts of the cat's body develop the darker colour, the remainder is white.

Which parts are colder?

Intelligent rats?

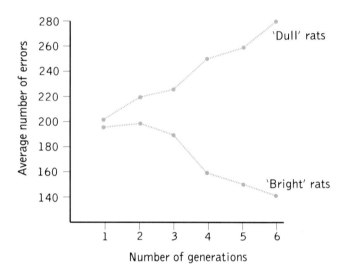

An experiment was carried out with rats learning their way through mazes. Those that learnt their way more quickly were mated and their young were again tested in the maze. The 'bright' rats were allowed to breed. This was continued for several generations. At the same time those rats that took longer to learn their way through the maze were also mated. This was also continued for several generations to produce a group of 'dull' rats. The results are shown in the graph.

Studies of identical twins

Since identical twins have the same genotypes, any differences they show in their characteristics should be due to the environment. Some interesting studies have compared twins from the same home with twins that have been separated from each other at a young age and brought up by different parents.

Difference in:	Identical twins reared together	Unlike twins reared together	Identical twins reared apart
Height (cm)	1.7	4.4	1.8
Weight (kg)	1.86	4.53	4.49
IQ tests	3.1	8.5	6.0

Average differences in characteristics between pairs of twins.

Changing leaves

These arrowleaf plants have been grown from the same root. They have then been grown in different conditions.

In damp soil

In shallow water with a gentle current

In deep water with a fast current

The Lysenko affair

Lysenko, a Russian scientist, believed in Lamarck's theory of evolution. This suggested that characteristics developed during the life of an organism would be passed on to the offspring. For instance, giraffes would stretch their necks to reach leaves on tall trees and their young would then be born with longer necks. He also believed that parts of the body falling into disuse would no longer be produced in offspring. To test this idea an experiment was carried out with mice. It was believed that they did not need tails. These were cut off from adult mice for several generations. However the young were still born with tails. Lysenko applied this idea to growing crops with disastrous consequences. He believed that cereal seeds kept at low temperatures would produce plants better able to grow in colder climates. For several years Russia had very poor harvests until Lysenko's ideas were discounted and seeds were selected from plants which had shown the more suitable features.

Blue or pink hydrangeas?

Hydrangea flowers will change colour depending on the soil. If the soil is acid they will be blue but if the soil is chalky they will be pink.

Banded snails

The banded snail, *Cepea nemoralis*, occurs in a number of different forms. The colours and numbers of the bands vary and some snails have no bands at all. The shell colour appears to vary with the type of habitat giving better camouflage to the snails. Do these snails change to match their background or are their genes different? Snails moved from one area to another do not change their colours.

Musical families?

Do brilliant musicians inherit this talent from their parents or is it due to the environment in which they are reared?

Johann Sebastian Bach (1685–1750), the well-known German composer and organist, came from a large family which included many talented musicians. This family spans many generations. His father taught him to play the violin and viola. His uncle, Johann Christoph Bach was a famous organist of his time. When Johann Sebastian was left an orphan, his uncle and aunt looked after him.

Johann Sebastian Bach married twice and had 20 children, three of whom grew up to become the most famous composers of their day.

Extension questions and activities

A Look at the information on page 52 about pairs of like and unlike twins. Put the results in a suitable graph.

a Which characteristic is most likely to be controlled by genes?

b Which characteristic is most likely to be controlled by the environment?

c Explain why results from identical twin studies can be used to distinguish between the effects of genes and the effects of the environment.

What will produce variations?

B

Dinosaurs are now extinct	All living things have DNA	Animals and plants live in every habitat in the world
Vertebrates have similar skeletons	Plants and animals have similar cells	Very old rocks have no fossil remains
Different species have different amounts and types of DNA	There are many different types of vertebrates	Fossils are found in rocks
Plants have similar life cycles	Giraffes have long necks	Finches have different shaped beaks

Either

write a letter to Darwin's opponents using any of these statements you consider relevant explaining why you think Darwin's theory of evolution was right;

or

write a letter to Darwin explaining why you think he was wrong.

C The table below shows the variation in blood groups of different racial types.

Population	Percentage of population with blood group			
	A	B	AB	O
Chinese	27	23	6	44
French	45	9	4	42
Indian	25	38	7	30
Nigerian	21	23	4	52
American Indian	22	0	0	78
US 'blacks'	27	21	4	48
US 'whites'	41	10	4	45
Welsh	35	10	3	52

a Blood group O is the most common in most races. In which population is a different group more common?

b Which blood group is the least common?

c What is different about the blood groups of the American Indians?

d It is claimed that by studying the blood groups of different races we can find out about movements of people from different countries in the past. Is there any evidence of this from the figures in the chart?

e What results would you expect if we carried out a similar survey in 100 years time?

D Genetically identical dandelion plants can be grown by cutting up their underground stem into many small pieces and placing each piece into a flower pot with soil or compost. What experiments could you carry out to find out which characteristics are determined by genes and which vary with environmental changes?

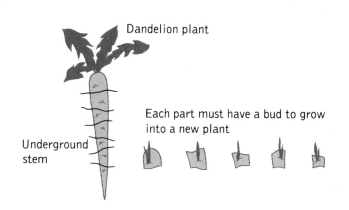

Dandelion plant

Each part must have a bud to grow into a new plant

Underground stem

Evidence or proof?

Before looking at these questions, you will need to read the pages on *Nature versus nurture*.

A Each characteristic of a plant and an animal could be placed into one of three groups.

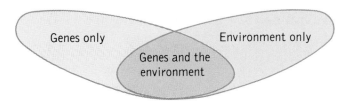

Genes only

Environment only

Genes and the environment

Here are some examples:
● flower colour in hydrangeas;
● 'bright' and 'dull' rats;
● height in humans;
You can add to this list from the previous pages.

Place each example from your list into one of the three groups above.

B You may say that both genes and the environment play a part in making a brilliant musician but how could you prove it? Many of the results from studies and experiments provide evidence to support a hypothesis. It can only be regarded as proof when the amount of evidence is overwhelming and there is nothing to contradict it. Decide for each example what evidence you have for placing it in that group. For example, you may have decided that weight in identical twins should be placed in the group, 'Genes and the environment determine the features'. Your evidence for this may be that:
● identical twins reared together had differences in their weight;
● this was even greater when they were reared apart;

● because identical twins had closer weights than unlike twins, the genes also played a part.
Now try to decide for the other examples the evidence you can find for the groups you have placed them in. Place the information in a table.

Characteristic	Group	Evidence
Musical ability		

C Choose one of your examples from the above lists and suggest what other evidence you would need before you would be able to say that you have proof.

D Why do you think the work of Mendel would be regarded as proof of how characteristics are inherited while the work of Darwin would be regarded as evidence for evolution but not proof?

E Read the article about Lysenko. This tells you something about Lamarck's ideas of evolution. In what ways does his theory differ from Darwin's? Suggest some characteristics that would be passed from one generation to the next if Lamarck's ideas were true, e.g. a weight-lifter would have children with large muscles. Can you think of any evidence to support Lamarck's theory of evolution?

Index